# TIMELESS TALES

# Legends

Retold by TANA REIFF

Illustrated by BILL BAYLIS

NEW READERS PRESS

Timeless Tales: Legends
ISBN 978-0-88336-273-0
Copyright © 1991 New Readers Press
New Readers Press
Division of ProLiteracy Worldwide
1320 Jamesville Avenue, Syracuse, New York 13210
www.newreaderspress.com

Printed in the United States of America
20  19  18  17  16  15  14  13  12  11  10  9

All proceeds from the sale of New Readers Press materials
support literacy programs in the United States and worldwide.

**Acquisitions Editor:** Elizabeth Costello
**Manuscript Editor:** Mark Legler
**Designer:** Patricia Ripple
**Illustrator:** Bill Baylis
**Cover Designer:** The WD Burdick Company
**Sponsoring Editor:** Marianne Ralbovsky

# Contents

# Introduction

Legends tell stories about people or animals. Some began as true stories. Then, over the years, people added things and blew up the facts. Soon, the legends grew far past what really happened. Some of the legends were never true. The stories just grew until they seemed real.

Some legends help explain the world. The many ups and downs of Anansi the spider helped explain the world to the people of West Africa. The native people of Mexico and the American Southwest tell stories of Don Coyote (kye-OH-tee). These stories tell about the ways this smart animal helped people.

Some legends become "tall tales." The old-time loggers of the North and West told stories of a giant named Paul Bunyan. Just for laughs, the loggers tried to top each other with each new story they made up. These stories were called "tall tales" because they went way past the truth.

Some legends come about when a person stands out from the crowd. Johnny Appleseed and Robin Hood were real people who lived very differently from others. King Arthur and Zal the White-Haired are two leaders who became the subjects of legends.

In many countries, legends are about magic little people. They may be called fairies, pixies, elves, brownies, or gnomes. But the most famous of all are the leprechauns (LEH-pra-KAHNZ) of Ireland. Who is to say whether they are real? The point is, it's fun to think there may be someone hiding nearby who can do magic.

Fun may be the true reason a legend is passed on. Tales of interesting people and special animals are just plain fun to read.

# Anansi, the Spider:
## How the World Got Wisdom

West Africa

 Anansi was a very smart spider.
Sometimes, however, he was not
as smart as he wanted people
to believe.

Way back when, Anansi was the only one
who knew everything. He knew how to do
everything. He knew all about everything.
He knew all there was to know about the
world. And he wanted to keep this wisdom
all to himself.

So Anansi put all the wisdom in the world into a pot. Now, this pot was made of clay. Anansi had to be careful not to break it. He didn't want the wisdom to fall out and get away from him.

"I'll hide this pot of wisdom," he said. "I'll carry it to the top of the tallest tree. Only I can climb that high. No one but I will ever reach the pot of wisdom."

Anansi picked up the pot. He tried to climb the tree. But the pot was too heavy. After all, it held all the wisdom in the world. What is more, Anansi's arms could not reach around the pot to hold onto a branch.

So Anansi moved the pot to his back.
Again, he tried to climb the tree. But he
couldn't climb with the pot in back, either.
It was still too heavy. After all, it held all the
wisdom in the world. Anansi could hold
onto a branch now, but the pot pulled him
backward. He fell to the ground, pot and all.

By this time Anansi was angry. Here he
was, with all the wisdom in the world. But
there was one important thing he did not
know. He did not know how to get the pot
to the top of the tree.

Anansi came up with one more idea. He
tied his webbing to the pot and climbed the
tree. He tried to pull the pot up with the
thread. But he just couldn't keep his legs
hooked to a branch. He fell out of the tree
and onto his head.

9

Now Anansi was so angry that he grabbed the pot and threw it to the ground. The pot crashed into millions of bits. All the wisdom in the world was lying on the ground, where anyone could find it.

In no time, word got out about the broken pot of wisdom. All the people of the world came running. They each took some wisdom to keep for themselves.

That, goes the story, is how the world got wisdom—and why wisdom is not all in one place.

# Don Coyote:
## How the World Got Fire

Mexico and the
Southwest United States

 When the people of the world got fire, they learned to use it in many ways. Fire helped people to cook, stay warm, have light, and make things.

But the legends say there was a time when people did not have fire. The world was dark. The people were hungry and cold. It was Don Coyote who gave them fire.

Don Coyote was the smartest animal ever. He knew of a place on the top of a mountain. A ball of fire was kept in a big pot up there. But Fire Beings watched the pot at all times. The three Fire Beings not only had fire, they were fire. And they kept the fire to themselves.

Don Coyote watched the Fire Beings as they watched the fire. They took turns. He waited for a chance to steal the fire and take it down the mountain. He waited and watched for days. Always, one Fire Being sat by the pot.

Then one morning, Don Coyote got his chance. "It's your turn to watch the fire," called one Fire Being to the next.

The next Fire Being was still asleep. So the first Fire Being left the fire to wake her up. She was gone only half a minute. But just that fast, Don Coyote ran to the pot. He picked it up by the handles, and took off down the mountain.

He didn't get far before the Fire Beings saw him. All three of them flew after Don Coyote. "Get back here with our fire!" they shouted. Don Coyote was fast. He kept ahead of the Fire Beings almost the whole way down.

But he was not fast enough. One of the Fire Beings got close to Don Coyote. She grabbed his tail. He kept on running, but the Fire Being burned the end of his tail. That is why, even today, the tip of a coyote's tail is white.

Don Coyote kept on running. He spotted Squirrel just below. "Catch this pot!" he called to Squirrel. He threw the pot. Squirrel caught it, and ran with the pot on his back. The pot was so hot that Squirrel's tail curled up. That is why, even today, the tail of a squirrel curls up and over its back.

The Fire Beings flew after Squirrel. Squirrel threw the pot of fire to Chipmunk. The Fire Beings flew after Chipmunk. One of them ran her claws down Chipmunk's back. That is why, even today, a chipmunk has three white lines down its back.

Chipmunk threw the pot of fire to Frog. The Fire Beings flew after Frog. One of them grabbed Frog's tail. Frog kept on running, but his tail broke off. That is why, even today, a frog has no tail.

Frog threw the pot of fire back to Don Coyote. Some flames flew out of the pot. They rose in the sky and became the stars. The biggest became the sun.

Don Coyote ran like the wind. The Fire Beings fell behind him. When he reached the bottom of the mountain, he threw the fire onto a pile of wood. The Fire Beings watched as the wood ate the fire. They wanted to get the fire out of the wood. But they didn't know how. They gave up and flew back up the mountain.

Don Coyote knew how to get fire out of wood. He showed the cold, hungry people how to do it. Whenever they needed fire, all they had to do was rub two sticks together.

And that is how Don Coyote gave fire to the world.

# Paul Bunyan and Babe, the Blue Ox

United States and Canada

 Paul Bunyan was born in Canada or Maine. No one is really sure where—only that it was up north.

Paul Bunyan was one big baby. He was 80 pounds at birth. His parents put his cradle in the ocean. When it rocked, it sent waves to shore that washed away whole towns.

Paul Bunyan just kept on growing. He ate 74 buckets of oatmeal for breakfast. He combed his beard with a pine tree. There was a space of 17 inches between his eyes. He was so tall, he couldn't see down to his own feet.

15

Big as he was, Paul Bunyan could move fast
and work well with his hands. So he became
a logger. As you may know, a logger is
someone who cuts down trees for wood. In
Paul Bunyan's day, the loggers worked hard
to clear forests. People needed room for
farms and houses. Paul could cut more trees,
and faster, than anyone alive.

One year, there was a very big winter
storm. They say the snow was 200 feet deep.
Not only that, the snow was blue. When it
finally melted, it made blue water. They say
that lakes are blue because of that melted
blue snow.

The Winter of the Blue Snow was the year Paul Bunyan found his famous friend, the ox. Paul went outside to get some wood for his fire. There he saw two little ears in the snow. He reached in and pulled out a baby ox. Like the snow, the animal was blue! Paul carried it home in his pocket and cared for it. He named the ox "Babe."

Even when Babe warmed up, he stayed blue. Babe grew and grew until he was as big as Paul. Babe could eat a wagonload of hay at one meal. When he walked, he set off earthquakes.

Paul and Babe worked together at the logging camp. The road leading out of the logging camp was crooked. It gave the men trouble as they drove wagons of wood out of the forest. So Paul Bunyan tied one end of the road to a tree. He tied Babe the blue ox to the other end of the road. Babe pulled and pulled. Sure enough, he made the road straight as a board.

After a while, Babe grew so big that he got kind of lazy. One time, he would not pull the logs down the road. He wanted to wait until there was snow on the ground so the logs would slide more easily.

Paul painted the road white. Thinking it was snow, Babe got right to work. He pulled the logs just fine and never knew there wasn't really snow on the road.

It took a lot of food to feed Babe. There was never enough. So Paul got one of his men to make a pair of big green glasses. Paul put the glasses on Babe and sent him outside. Now the white-painted road looked like grass to Babe. He ate for days.

A few years later, some people wanted to put a line between Canada and the United States. They began to dig a river. The work was going slowly. Then the man in charge made a deal with Paul Bunyan. "Dig out a river bed in three weeks," said the man. "If you do, I'll give you a million dollars."

That sounded good to Paul, so he and Babe got to work. First, they made a shovel as big as a house. Digging with that tool made the work go fast.

In three weeks, they were finished. Rain filled the riverbed with water. The dirt Paul had dug out made big piles over in Vermont. Those piles are called the Green Mountains.

Now it was time for Paul to get paid. But the man would not pay him.

Paul picked up the shovel as big as a house. He shoveled some dirt back into the river.

"All right, all right," said the man. "I will pay you half a million."

Paul shoveled more dirt back into the river.

"All right, all right," said the man. "I will pay you two-thirds of a million."

Paul shoveled more dirt back into the river. When he had shoveled a thousand times, the man yelled, "Stop! Stop! I will pay you your million dollars."

Paul Bunyan got his money. The thousand shovels of dirt became known as the Thousand Islands.

Another time, Paul was asked to clear the trees in North Dakota so the people could plant farms. Paul's ax was huge. It was made out of 77 axes all melted together. The handle was made from a tree trunk. The ax was so big it could cut down 20 trees at once.

Paul cut down the trees in North Dakota in one month. But the stumps were still there. There were millions of them. They stuck out six inches above the ground.

"We can't plant farms with those stumps there," said the man who had hired Paul. "You'll have to get rid of them."

Paul had an idea. He knew that Babe hated to get his feet wet. So Paul filled the whole state with water. That made the ground soft. Then he sent Babe out into it. Babe tiptoed from one stump to the next, never stepping in the water. Of course, Babe was so heavy that he pushed the stumps right down into the ground.

Ever since, they say, you won't see a tree stump in North Dakota. You will, however, see miles and miles of farms, thanks to Paul Bunyan.

# Johnny Appleseed

United States

 There once was a man named John Chapman. He was born in the eastern part of the United States. As a child, he loved the flowers that grow on apple trees in the spring. He would pick them and smell them. Sometimes he would eat them. When the apples came, he loved those even more.

When John Chapman grew up, he went to school. He learned a great deal. His family wanted him to make lots of money.

But John had other ideas. He had never lost his strong love for apples. He wanted to find a way for people all over the country to have apples.

By this time, the Chapmans had moved toward the west, to Pennsylvania. A great many apple trees were growing there. In the fall, the apples were pressed to make juice. John went around to the apple presses. He asked to keep what was left after the juice was made. In the presses were apple seeds. He took the seeds and 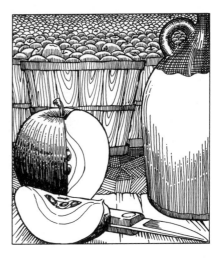 laid them out to dry in the sun. The next spring he packed the dried seeds into big grain sacks.

Then he set out toward the west and south. He had one idea in mind—to plant those apple seeds. He made it his job in life to plant the trees that would bear apples for the people.

John didn't wear shoes. He dressed in the empty grain sacks. He slept under the stars. He cooked his meals over an open fire. When it was time to move on, he put his cooking pan on his head. That was his hat. In all kinds of weather, he walked along with the sacks of apple seeds. People began calling him Johnny Appleseed.

He would stop in this place or that to plant a grove of apple trees. He would wait to make sure the seeds came up. Then he would walk on to another place. Sometime later, he would come back to check on the new trees. He enjoyed tasting the apples, knowing they were there because of him. Over the years, Johnny Appleseed covered a lot of ground. Apple trees grew wherever he had been.

Next time you eat an apple, think of Johnny Appleseed. Some people say it is because of him that apples grow almost everywhere in the United States.

# King Arthur

England

 When Arthur was born, an old magician named Merlin took him away to live with another family. The boy grew up not knowing he was the son of a king.

Arthur was still a child when his real father, the king, died. The question was, who would take over the throne? The king had a daughter, but she could not rule. At that time, a girl could not become queen unless she married a king. Only Merlin knew the king had a son. The people prayed for a new king.

Then the magic began. Out of nowhere appeared a block of stone. It sat in the yard of a grand old church. Stuck in the stone was a sword like the ones most of the men used for fighting. Around the stone were these words: *Whoever can pull the sword from this stone is the true king.*

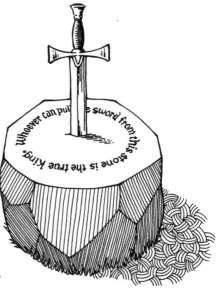

On New Year's Day, men from all over came to play fighting games. Each tried his luck at pulling the sword from the stone. Young Arthur, who was about 15 years old, came along with his brother, Kay. He did not know about the sword in the stone.

When they got there, Kay saw that he had left his sword at home. He wanted it for the games. So he asked young Arthur to go home and get it.

Arthur got ready to leave. Then he spotted the sword stuck in the stone.

"My brother cannot be without a sword," said Arthur. "Maybe this one will do." He walked over and with no trouble at all pulled the sword from the stone.

Just then, the men came back. What a surprise to see Arthur holding the sword! "How did you get that out?" they asked. "None of us could pull out the sword! We shall put it back in and watch you pull it out."

They put the sword back in the stone. One by one, all the men tried to pull out the sword. But it wouldn't move an inch. No one could get it out of the stone.

Then it was Arthur's turn. Once again, he pulled the sword right out of the stone as if he did this every day.

"You are the true king!" the people shouted. "King Arthur is our new king!" They held a big parade in the street. They were so happy. At last they had found their king! All the while, Merlin the Magician sat back and smiled.

Arthur ruled from the Great Hall in Camelot. When he turned 20, he decided it was time to take a wife. "Who would you like to marry?" Merlin the Magician asked him.

"The fair maid named Guinevere (GWIN-uh-VEER)," Arthur answered.

Merlin went to ask Guinevere's father for her hand. Her father agreed. He was happy for his daughter to marry the good king.

The wedding day came. Arthur and Guinevere were married before a large crowd. Guinevere looked more beautiful than Arthur had ever seen her. A crown was placed on her head. Guinevere was now the queen.

On the day of the wedding, the men ate together in the Great Hall. In the center was a round table with 150 chairs. "Who shall sit at this Round Table?" King Arthur asked Merlin.

"The finest knights in Camelot," Merlin answered. "These shall be the men who will fight for you."

"All of you, hear me!" said King Arthur. "Take your places at the Round Table."

They all sat down. Then they all lifted their drinks in a toast.

"We shall today make a promise!" said King Arthur. "From this day on, we shall defend the weak and fight for all that is good. This shall be our way and our work. We shall be the greatest knights that ever lived!"

And so they were. They fought many battles. They helped many people. King Arthur and his Knights of the Round Table live on in stories that are still told today.

# Robin Hood

England

 Robin Hood grew up in the forest. Living there made him very sharp with a bow and arrow. But one time he killed a man with his bow and arrow. That made Robin Hood an outlaw.

Then Robin learned of a whole band of outlaws who lived in Sherwood Forest. They ate wonderful feasts of deer meat that they took from the king's land. And they robbed and killed anyone who came along.

Robin Hood joined this band of outlaws. When they saw how good he was with a bow and arrow, they made him their leader.

"We shall change our ways a bit," Robin told his merry band. "No more shall you kill the people you rob. We shall never hurt a woman or child. We shall look only for rich men. When we find one, we will bring him back to have dinner with us."

They rode their horses to the forest path. They waited there until a man came along riding a fine horse and wearing fine clothes.

"Hello!" called Little John, who was really the biggest of the men. "Come along and have dinner with us."

"Thank you," said the rich man. "I am in need of a good meal."

The rich man went along to the merry band's forest home. They all ate a fine dinner together. Then Robin Hood said, "How much gold do you have with you?"

The rich man opened his coat. Out poured a pile of gold coins.

"The cost of your dinner is half the coins," said Robin Hood. "The rest you may keep. You may be sure that we will give your money to people who need it."

The rich man was surprised. But what could he do? He turned over the coins to Robin Hood.

"Thank you," said Robin Hood. "It is better to give than to take. Remember, you ate well here. And now you have a good story to tell your children."

The next day the merry band of outlaws brought back a man who worked for the king. Again, they fed him. Then Robin Hood asked, "How much money do you have with you?"

"Why, none at all," said the man. "Not a cent."

Robin did not believe him. He tore open the man's coat. There he found 100 gold coins. This time, Robin Hood kept all the gold coins, not just half of them.

"I would have taken only half your money," said Robin. "But because you lied, I will take it all."

They sent the man on his way without hurting him. Then Robin Hood rode off to the forest home of an old woman. He knew her from when he was a boy. She was poor but had given him cookies every time he passed her house.

"I give you gold coins, good woman," said Robin Hood. "May you live a long and happy life."

This is how Robin Hood and the merry band of outlaws worked. They took from the rich and gave to the poor. They had many ways of doing this. And their tricks and pranks made them famous for hundreds of years to come.

# Zal and the Wonder Bird

Persia (Iran)

Many, many years ago a man named Sahm was the best fighter in Persia. The king put Sahm in charge of a big part of the country. Sahm lived well and had a wonderful wife. Still, he was not happy because he had no children.

Sahm waited many years. At last, he and his wife had a baby boy named Zal. The child was born in good health. He had ten fingers and ten toes. He had a beautiful face. But there was something odd about Zal. He had white hair, like an old person's.

Sahm was afraid of the boy. He was also afraid that people would laugh at him for having a child with white hair. So he took the baby to the bottom of a mountain and left him there.

The Wonder Bird lived up on that mountain. The bird had magic power. She spotted the baby, flew down, and picked him up. Then the Wonder Bird carried Zal back to her nest.

As she flew, she heard a voice. "Care for this child," said the voice. "Someday he will be a great person. His son will be the greatest man that Persia will ever know."

The baby was hungry. The Wonder Bird brought him food. She told her baby birds not to hurt him. The Wonder Bird raised Zal as her own.

 As Zal grew, he lived like a bird. He could almost fly among the rocks of the mountain. He knew the stars of the night sky. He knew nothing about how people lived.

Years went by. Zal's real father, Sahm, never got over what he had done to the baby. One night, Sahm had a dream. In his dream he heard a voice. "Your son is alive," said the voice. "You must go and get him back."

So Sahm sent out the army to look for Zal. They found him at the top of the mountain. "Your father has sent us to take you home," said the leader of the army.

"This is my home," said Zal.

"You must go," said the Wonder Bird. She pulled three feathers from her wing. She gave them to Zal to take with him. "Keep these feathers," she said. "If you are ever in trouble, throw one feather into a fire. I will come and help you."

Zal went home to Sahm. Sahm tried to make up for all the time his son had been away. He made Zal a prince. Zal became a good leader for much of Persia.

One day Zal set out to see more of the land. He came upon a place his father had warned him about. The ruler was not a bad man, but his grandfather had been very bad. Ever since, the rest of Persia hated everyone who lived there.

The ruler had a kind, beautiful daughter. Her name was Rudabeh (ROO-duh-BAY). Under the moon that night, Zal and Rudabeh fell in love.

At first, they kept their love a secret. But they wanted to get married. They each told their parents, who were not happy about the idea. But Rudabeh's parents loved her very much. And Zal's parents would do anything for him now. So after much doing, the two families let Zal and Rudabeh marry.

How happy they were!

But their joy was not to last. Rudabeh became very sick. There was nothing the doctors could do for her. Zal was sad beyond words. He had waited so long to be with Rudabeh. Now it seemed the end was near.

Then Zal remembered the Wonder Bird's feathers. He ran to get them. He came back into Rudabeh's room and threw one feather into the fireplace. All of a sudden, everything got dark. Zal and Rudabeh heard the sound of rushing wings. The Wonder Bird was in the room!

"You have no need to be sad!" said the Wonder Bird. She gave Zal a magic cure for Rudabeh. She also left behind another feather so that Zal would always have three.

In no time at all, Rudabeh was feeling fine. About a year later, she and Zal had a baby boy. His name was Rustem, and he became a great hero. Even today, some say the son of Rudabeh and Zal the White-Haired was the strongest and best fighter that Persia ever knew.

# William Tell

Switzerland

 A long time ago, the country we call Switzerland was three small countries. Times were hard. Taxes were high. Anyone with fish, game, or crops had to give most of it to the lords of the land. The lords kept it all for themselves. Anyone who did not do what the lords asked could be killed. The people lived in deep fear.

In one of these three lands lived a man named William Tell. He could shoot arrows with his bow better than anyone else. People knew him as a brave hunter.

One day he and his son went into town. They saw a crowd gathered in the square. There, in the middle, was the meanest lord of all. He had hung his hat on a high pole. He was making all the people fall down on their knees in front of the hat.

William Tell saw what was going on. He and the boy started walking on past the hat on the pole.

"Stop!" called the lord. "You did not fall to your knees!"

"I will not," said William Tell.

"Oh, no?" cried the lord. "Then you shall do something else for me instead!"

The mean lord placed an apple on the boy's head. He made the boy stand in front of a tree. "There!" he laughed. "You think you are so brave! See if you can shoot that apple off your son's head."

William Tell picked up his bow. He set an arrow in it.

The boy was afraid.
He stood very still.
He could not see the
apple. He only hoped
that his father would
hit the apple and
not him.

William Tell drew his
bow. He fixed his eyes
on the apple. PING!
The arrow flew out of
the bow and right into
the apple.

The boy moved away.
The arrow held the
apple to the tree trunk.
The crowd let out a
big cheer.

But William Tell was not yet out of trouble.
The lord saw that he had another arrow.
"Why do you hide an arrow in your shirt?"
asked the lord.

"If I had hurt my son, I would have used
the second arrow on you," said William Tell.

That made the lord very angry. "You should
not have told me that," he said. "Now I must
lock you up." And he took the arrow away
from Tell.

43

William Tell sent his son home and went with the lord. The lord and his men took William Tell in a boat to the castle. But just as they got to the castle, William Tell jumped out of the boat.

He ran into the forest. It was getting dark. The lord and his men could not find him.

William Tell knew they would look for him the next day. He worked all night making another arrow. When he finished, it was very straight and very sharp.

Early the next morning, William Tell made his way back to the castle. He hid and waited. When he saw the lord's fine horse, he put the arrow in his bow. He pulled back the bow. PING! The arrow hit the mean lord in the heart.

It was the first and last time William Tell used his bow on a person. But it was the beginning of a free land. The people heard what William Tell had done. A war broke out against all the lords. The three small countries joined together as one. The new country was named Switzerland and is free to this day.

# The Leprechaun and the Pot of Gold

Ireland

In a place called Ireland they say
that leprechauns are tiny little
people who make shoes for the
fairies. They live and work alone
in out-of-the-way places. They
each wear a red jacket, a hat,
and a leather apron. They each
have big, pointed ears and a round nose.
They are never more than three inches tall.

Best of all, every leprechaun keeps a pot
of gold hidden under the ground. If you can
catch a leprechaun, you are very lucky. If
you can keep your eyes on him, he must lead
you to his pot of gold.

One time a young girl was walking in the forest. She was looking for flowers to pick. As she walked, she heard the sound of a hammer. Tap, tap, tap. It wasn't very loud. It sounded like a very small hammer.

"I must be close to a leprechaun," said the girl.

She followed the sound. It was coming from behind a big tree. She walked up to the tree. She peeked around the wide trunk. Sure enough, there was a leprechaun! He was making a pair of shoes for a fairy.

The young girl reached out her hand. She grabbed the little leprechaun. "I've got you!" she screamed.

"Sure and you do," said the leprechaun. "I guess now you want me to lead you to my pot of gold."

"That's the rule," said the girl. "If I catch a leprechaun, he must lead me to his pot of gold."

"There is another rule," said the leprechaun. "You may not take your eyes off me. Not even for a second. You must keep your eyes on me at all times until we reach the gold."

The girl didn't move her eyes from the leprechaun. "Now, where is the gold?" she asked. "Is it under the rainbow?"

"Perhaps it is, perhaps it isn't," said the leprechaun. "But we'll never find the gold if that big tree falls on you."

The girl kept her eyes on the leprechaun. "You are trying to trick me into looking away," she said. "I've heard that about leprechauns. But I know better. I won't fall for your tricks."

"Walk over into that field of flowers," said the leprechaun, pointing. "I'll take you to the pot of gold. Watch out! There's a rabbit behind you and he's going to jump on your head!"

The girl almost looked behind her. But she didn't. She kept her eyes right on the leprechaun. "Let's keep on walking," she said.

It began to rain. As fast as it began, the rain stopped. "Look!" shouted the leprechaun. "There's a rainbow!"

A rainbow! The girl felt sure the pot of gold must be there! She looked up toward the sky. But she saw no rainbow. Then she knew she had been tricked.

She looked back down to her hands. The leprechaun was gone! The girl looked all around her, but the little person was not there. By looking for the rainbow, the girl had taken her eyes off the leprechaun. The pot of gold was not to be hers.

In one way or another, the leprechaun always gets away. But people keep trying to find the one that will lead to a pot of gold.